GCSE AQA English
The Workbook
Reading Non-Fiction and Media Texts

This book is for anyone doing **GCSE AQA A English** at higher level.

It contains lots of **tricky questions** designed to hone your **reading skills** — because that's the only way you'll get any **better**.

It's also got some daft bits in to try and make the whole experience at least vaguely entertaining for you.

What CGP is all about

Our sole aim here at CGP is to produce the highest quality books — carefully written, immaculately presented and dangerously close to being funny.

Then we work our socks off to get them out to you — at the cheapest possible prices.

CONTENTS

Section One — Purpose and Audience

The Audience 1
The Purpose of the Text 2
Informative and Entertaining Texts 3
Texts that Argue, Persuade or Advise 4
Formal Style and Informal Style 5
Personal Tone and Impersonal Tone 6

Section Two — Following an Argument

Following an Argument 7
Evaluating an Argument 8
Facts and Opinions 9
Generalisations and Counter-arguments 10
Rhetoric and Bias 11

Section Three — Presentation and Layout

Headlines, Subheadings and Straplines 12
Graphics and Captions 13
Text Positioning 14
Bullet Points, Numbered Lists and Colour 15
Font Styles and Formatting 16

Section Four — Writing Techniques

Descriptive Language 17
Metaphors, Similes and Analogies 18
Personification, Alliteration and Onomatopoeia 19
Irony and Sarcasm 20
Technical and Emotive Language 21
Tabloid Newspaper Language 22
Structure 23

Section Five — Exam Techniques

P.E.E. 24
Writing in Paragraphs 25
Reading with Insight 26
Comparing Texts 27

Section Six — Sample Exam

Sample Exam — Questions 28
Sample Exam — Item A 29
Sample Exam — Item B 30
Mark Scheme — Question 1 (a) 32
Sample Answers — Question 1 (a) 33
Mark Scheme — Question 1 (b) 34
Sample Answers — Question 1 (b) 35
Mark Scheme — Question 2 (a) 36
Sample Answers — Question 2 (a) 37
Mark Scheme — Question 2 (b) 38
Sample Answers — Question 2 (b) 39

Section Seven — Practice Exam

Practice Exam — Questions 40
Practice Exam — Item A 41
Practice Exam — Item B 42

Published by Coordination Group Publications Ltd.

Editors:
Tim Burne
Katherine Craig
Charley Darbishire
Katherine Reed
Edward Robinson
Jennifer Underwood

Contributors:
Karen Fallows
Roland Haynes
Alison Smith

ISBN: 978 1 84146 862 4

With thanks to Rachel Selway and Sue Hirst for the proofreading.
With thanks to Laura Phillips for the copyright research.

Groovy website: www.cgpbooks.co.uk

Jolly bits of clipart from CorelDRAW®

Printed by Elanders Hindson Ltd, Newcastle upon Tyne.

The Audience

Q1 For each sentence, circle the word which best describes the audience it is aimed at. The first one has been done for you.

a) "Do you yearn for a simpler, more reliable way of managing your finances?"

children / **adults**

b) "When buying a used car, try to get as much information from the dealer as you can."

experts / novices

c) "China is one of the fastest growing economies in the world."

tourists / business people

Q2 For each of the extracts below, write down the type of audience you think it is intended for, and briefly explain how you know.

a) "This position requires a flexible approach and a 'can-do' attitude."

....

....

b) "Before applying for a course, do plenty of research on the institution and its reputation."

....

....

Q3 What sort of people would you expect to read an article from these publications?

a) *The Rough Guide to Turkey* ....

b) *The Times Educational Supplement* ....

c) *The Big Book of Car Games* ....

Q4 Read the text below and answer the question underneath. MINI-ESSAY QUESTION

Are you looking for a cool summer job?

We've got loads of temporary vacancies with no experience required!

All you need is some free time, a positive attitude and plenty of energy. If you've got your own wheels that's even better!

Picking... packing... stacking... waitering... waitressing... waitering... and TONS of others!

With Spondon Summer Jobs you can:
• *gain great work experience*
• *make a few quid*
• *make new friends*

Whatever you fancy, we can sort you out with a job that suits you down to the ground.
Interested? Call Jackie on
0547 262 626.

How does the advert aim to appeal directly to younger readers? Look at:
• the language used
• the content of the advertisement
• the font styles and presentation used

You'll need to use a separate sheet of paper to answer the mini-essay questions.

The Purpose of the Text

Q1 Draw lines to match each type of text to its main purpose.

a) "Who could disagree with the fact that children should eat healthily?"

b) "As the train moved south, first crawling, then increasing to a steady gallop, the scenery gradually changed from the flat and drab to the dramatic and beautiful."

c) "Shop around for the best quote — some insurers are much more expensive than others."

d) "Tomorrow, there will be scattered showers in the north-west."

To entertain

To inform

To persuade

To advise

Q2 Put each of the following types of text in the correct place in the table, based on their main purpose. The first one has been done for you. You may find that some of these fit into more than one column.

a charity advertisement	an article about the Industrial Revolution
a cake recipe	a film review
a newspaper editorial	an agony aunt column in a magazine
a leaflet from a political party	an instruction manual for a computer
a cartoon in a newspaper	a leaflet with tips on how to give up smoking

Texts that inform	Texts that entertain	Texts that argue or persuade	Texts that advise
		a charity advertisement	

Q3 Read the extract below, which was taken from a leaflet about a local election, then answer the question about it.

It is high time the people of this parish took a stand. We must tell the council: "enough is enough — *no more tax increases*."

Time after time we have been told that this is the final time it will happen; and then what do we find? Another council tax increase. We are told that "vital improvements" will be made to local roads and services — yet time and again they fail to deliver.

Are we really expected to believe things will be any different this time?

We must send out a clear message that we will not be taken for fools again. By voting for Sandy Green in the forthcoming council elections you can put an end to the growing amount of money leaving your pocket for no good reason.

What persuasive techniques does the writer of this text use to try to achieve her purpose?

MINI-ESSAY QUESTION

Informative and Entertaining Texts

Q1   Put an **I** next to the statements that are informative, and an **E** next to the entertaining ones.

a)   "Steven Morrissey was born in Manchester on 22nd May 1959."   ☐

b)   "The gig was absolute mayhem. Swathes of bodies ebbed and flowed in a sea of delirium — enjoyment and a survival instinct competed for my attention."   ☐

c)   "The next event at Spark Bridge village hall is a performance by Jim Dodd and the Budgies, at 7.30 pm on December 12th."   ☐

Is that all I'm here for — your entertainment?

Q2   Pick out three words or phrases that are entertaining and three words or phrases that are informative from the text below.

> Thai food can be startlingly hot, so watch out! The chefs round here get through chillies like you wouldn't believe — though some relief comes from the creamy coconut milk that tames the fire of the burning hot curries. For the adventurous, the colourful cuisine of the north-east makes liberal use of lime juice, garlic and fermented fish, contributing to its distinctive pungency.

Informative words or phrases:

1)   ....

2)   ....

3)   ....

Entertaining words or phrases:

1)   ....

2)   ....

3)   ....

Q3   Read the two texts below, then say which text is informative and which text is entertaining. Write a brief explanation for each answer.

a)
> The Battle of Hastings was fought on October 14th 1066 on a field near Hastings in East Sussex. Led by William the Conqueror, it was the Normans' most important victory over the Anglo-Saxons, led by King Harold II, in their invasion of England.

This text is **entertaining / informative** because ....

....

....

b)
> The battle was furious and bloody, with vast numbers of soldiers being brutally slain. At one stage the English were fooled into thinking they had won the battle, and stormed towards their enemy, only to find themselves ambushed and mercilessly pummelled.

This text is **entertaining / informative** because ....

....

....

Texts that Argue, Persuade or Advise

Q1   Draw lines to match each statement below to its purpose.

a)   "The barbaric practice of bear-baiting must be stopped completely and immediately."   **To argue**

b)   "If you want to make a difference, there are many organisations you can sign up to."   **To persuade**

c)   "By joining our march and signing this petition, you will be helping to put an end to this disgraceful act of cruelty."   **To advise**

Q2   For each extract, write down whether you think its purpose is to argue, to persuade or to advise, and briefly explain your answer.

a)   The bad language used by youngsters today is disgraceful. What's more, they seem to have no respect for authority, and society is a worse place as a result.

Purpose .... Explanation ....

....

....

b)   A stern telling-off after bad behaviour is often all that is needed to ensure your child grows into a responsible, considerate individual.

Purpose .... Explanation ....

....

....

Q3   Read the extract from a leaflet below and then answer the question about it underneath.

Come to Oxton Aquarium — you'll have a whale of a time!

Oxton Aquarium is the only place in the county where you can see local and exotic species of fish and sea mammals all in one place.

Experience the magic of the deep as you are surrounded by the underwater world. You could be eyed up by an octopus, shaken by a shark or peered at by pike!

Whatever your age, you're guaranteed a fantastic time.

Entry costs: Adult — £6   Child — £3   Family ticket — £15

Oxton Aquarium — a great family day out!

Before you dive in to answering this question, make sure you're clear about what the writer's purpose is.

How does the presentation and choice of language help the leaflet to achieve its purpose?

MINI-ESSAY QUESTION

Section One — Purpose and Audience

Formal Style and Informal Style

Q1 For each pair of sentences, underline the more formal sentence.

Sorry Sir, we don't accept credit cards — you're going to have to go in the kitchen and wash up.

a) "Sorry! We don't take credit cards."
"Customers are advised that we do not accept credit cards."

b) "It is essential to ensure you have the correct tools before proceeding."
"Check you've got the proper kit to hand before you go any further."

c) "Worried about rising debts? We've got all the info you need to sort your finances out."
"If you have financial complications, contact our advisors at the following address."

Q2 Put each language feature in the correct column, based on where you would usually expect to find it.

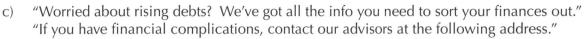

non-standard English
standard English
complex sentences
simple sentences
chatty tone
serious tone
contractions (e.g. "don't")
impersonal style
personal style
humour

Formal texts	Informal texts

Q3 The text below is taken from a travel journal. Is the style of the text formal or informal? Write down three pieces of evidence from the text that back up your answer.

At this point I was starting to get a tad — how shall I put it? — narked off. It's one thing being patient, accepting the fact that things don't always go to plan and that now and then delays just happen. It's quite another to be told, after paying good money for a ticket on the grounds that it's taking you to Town A, that apparently for no good reason we're taking a little detour through Village B, River C and Swamp D.

I was finding it more and more difficult to follow what I had figured was the local way of dealing with difficulties — smiling and pretending to find the grim industrial scenery interesting.

The style is .... because:

1) ....

2) ....

3) ....

I like your style...

The style a writer chooses has to be appropriate for the intended audience. Keep this in mind in the exam — it'll make your answer a lot more relevant than if you just describe what the style is.

Personal Tone and Impersonal Tone

Q1   Write a **P** for "personal" or an **I** for "impersonal" to describe
       the tone that would usually be created by each technique.

   a) written in first person ☐   e) lots of facts used ☐

   b) written in passive voice ☐   f) sounds emotional ☐

   c) openly biased ☐   g) slang used ☐

   d) neutral tone ☐   h) formal language used ☐

Q2   Decide whether the text below has a personal or an impersonal tone.
       Find three pieces of evidence from the text to support your answer.

> There is a growing feeling that the situation concerning air pollution needs to be addressed.
> The number of individuals suffering from breathing problems in the city has been steadily
> increasing for years, with levels of carbon dioxide and other greenhouse gases soaring to
> new heights. Possible solutions are to be discussed at the next city council meeting.

The tone is **personal** / **impersonal** because:

1) ....

2) ....

3) ....

Q3   Use the following extract from an agony aunt column to answer
       the questions at the bottom of the page.

> Dear Rowena
>
> You poor thing, you're really down in the dumps, aren't you? I know it's hard to believe but your
> life will improve — you just need to take control over things again. Concentrate on what you
> used to be like, when you were more confident and enjoying life.
>
> One thing that's definitely worth a shot is consulting a career guidance counsellor. If you haven't
> got time for this then there are plenty of books on choosing the right job that I can recommend.
>
> The main thing to remember is that you're the boss of your own life — so take charge!

   a) What techniques does the writer use to create a friendly, personal style in her writing?   MINI-ESSAY QUESTION

   b) How does this personal tone make the writing well suited to the target audience?   MINI-ESSAY QUESTION

Following an Argument

Q1 Read the following letter to the editor of the *Daily Muncaster* local newspaper.
Then answer the questions which follow.

Dear Sir,

I was horrified to read your article about the new soft drink "Swampy Water" being served in the tuck shop at Muncaster Primary School. This dangerous fad for drinking green, gungy water is clearly idiotic. Firstly, young children might get confused and think it's all right to drink *real* swamp water. I know from my time in the Territorial Army that this can make you very ill indeed. Secondly, "Swampy Water" is full of unhealthy sugar and additives — how else would it be that lurid green colour? Last but not least, the drink is expensive and means children don't have money left over to buy normal, healthy snacks. To conclude, "Swampy Water" should be removed from the tuck shop at Muncaster Primary School immediately.

Yours sincerely,
Gerry Bowness

a) What is the **main** argument of the letter? Tick the correct option below.

☐ Drinking swamp water can make you ill.

☐ "Swampy Water" is unhealthy because it contains additives and sugar.

☐ "Swampy Water" shouldn't be on sale in Muncaster Primary School.

b) Write down three points the writer makes to support his argument.
Write them using your own words.

1. ....

2. ....

3. ....

Q2 Read the following text then answer the question which follows.

I love the colour pink. I love birds. I really love flamingos. How could anyone dislike them? They're the most fascinating, mysterious and beautiful birds in the world! That's why I'm starting a campaign to persuade people to sponsor flamingos in zoos. By donating a few pounds, people can help fund the setting up of breeding programmes for rare flamingo species. The head keeper at my local zoo, Jane Sutton says, "Flamingos really are wonderful animals. Any donations would be much appreciated."

The table below shows the techniques used by the writer in their argument.
Fill in the table by picking out examples of each technique.

Technique	Example from text
repetition of words / phrases	
rhetorical question	
expert opinion	
exaggeration	

Evaluating an Argument

Q1   Which of the following would be **bad** to use in an argument? Tick the correct answers.

☐ inconsistencies   ☐ irony

☐ formal tone   ☐ factual inaccuracies

☐ out-of-date examples   ☐ points backed up with examples

☐ confusing explanations   ☐ persuasive language techniques

Q2   Read the following text. Describe one good point and one bad point about the way the author has written her argument.

> The greatest television presenter of all time is Terry Wogan. When he first appeared on television in 1865, Wogan astonished everyone with his energy, enthusiasm and sparkling wit. He had a star quality which all previous television presenters lacked. Who could fail to be charmed by him?

A **good** point about this argument is ....

....

....

A **bad** point about this argument is ....

....

....

Q3   Read the notice below and answer the question underneath.

Volunteers Needed for Salem Street Neighbourhood Group

No one wants to find litter and dog dirt on the pavement outside their front door. No one wants to have graffiti scratched on their car. No one wants to be woken up in the middle of the night by loud music or people arguing in the street. But, sadly, these things happen all the time in Salem Street. We all deserve to live in a **pleasant, safe, clean** street. And if we join together **we can make it happen**.

- A committee of Salem Street residents is being formed to look at issues like anti-social behaviour, litter and noise levels. It's an opportunity for **us**, the people who live in Salem Street, to be proactive and **improve our community**.

- Similar street committees in the Runford area have proved **very effective** in reducing anti-social behaviour, e.g. Midden Avenue, which used to suffer from high levels of litter and graffiti, is now a very clean, pleasant street.

- Helping with the committee won't take up much of your time — but it will make a **big difference** to Salem Street. Come along and find out more about the committee at our first meeting in **Rixy's Bingo Hall, 8pm, 16th May**.

How effectively does this notice persuade? Write about:

MINI-ESSAY QUESTION

- examples the writer uses to persuade the reader
- language devices the writer uses
- whether the leaflet achieves its purpose

Not bad, shame about the ranting...

When evaluating an argument, try and think of good and bad points about it. It's important to back up your points with examples though. Just saying, "this argument is rubbish" won't do.

Facts and Opinions

Q1 Write down whether the following statements are opinions, facts or false facts.

a) London is the capital city of the UK. ....

b) Glasgow would be a better capital city of Scotland than Edinburgh. ....

c) Manchester is the capital city of England. ....

Q2 Read the statements below. For each one, say whether you think it is a fact or an opinion and explain your choice.

It's not always clear if something is a fact or an opinion — you have to work it out for yourself.

a) "Water boils at 100 degrees Celsius."

....

....

b) "As Madonna gets older, her music gets better."

....

....

Q3 Read the text below. It was taken from a newspaper article.
After you've read it, answer the questions below.

We're All Getting Older
Edward Lightburn
From The Daily Splurge, Thursday 2nd March 2006

We're all living longer and longer. In 1900 in the USA, people could expect to reach 47 years. That was the average life expectancy. In 2000 it was 77 years and the trend is continuing. It might not be long until most people live 'til they're in their nineties, or even over one hundred.

What are we all going to be doing when we're eighty-something? At the moment, old people don't really get a good deal. As soon as they're too troublesome for their families, they get booted out of home and shipped off to the nearest "care home". And at these places, they'll be patronised, prodded and poked like sick animals: "Does Sarah want her din-dins now? It's her favourite..." It's not something to look forward to, is it?

It used to be that the elderly were respected for their wisdom. Now they're treated like the waste product of society, thrown out and left to rot in their care homes; the landfill sites of modern British humanity.

a) Write down two facts and two opinions from the text.

Well, I wanted to do something special for your 130th...

Facts:

1. ....

2. ....

Opinions:

1. ....

2. ....

b) What do you think the author's attitude to old people is?
Use evidence from the text to back up your answer.

MINI-ESSAY QUESTION

Generalisations and Counter-arguments

Q1 Tick the statements which are generalisations.

a) Gardening programmes on TV are all aimed at older viewers. ☐

b) There are different types of rose you can grow in your garden. ☐

c) My Aunt Daphne has a crush on Alan Titchmarsh. ☐

d) Alan Titchmarsh is adored by women everywhere. ☐

Aunt Daphne was the notorious 'Gardener's World' streaker.

Q2 What is a counter-argument?

....

....

Q3 Read the following article and then answer the questions which follow.

> Film critics usually dismiss 40s movie heart-throb Robert Mitchum as a dumb hunk of an actor. They claim his sleepy-eyed, laidback performances were lazy and lacklustre. They argue that he never took risks with his acting and assume that he lacked the technical acting ability of other 40s stars like Spencer Tracy and Laurence Olivier.
>
> But how can anybody who has seen his terrifying performance as a murderous preacher in 'The Night of the Hunter' claim that Mitchum never took risks? How can anybody who has seen his touching, vulnerable performance in 'Ryan's Daughter' claim he had no technical acting ability?
>
> The work of many other 1940s movie stars now looks out-of-date and hammy. But Mitchum's films have aged well — the naturalism and humour of his acting are truly immortal.

a) Which of the following quotes from the article sums up the writer's attitude to Robert Mitchum? Tick the correct one.

☐ "his sleepy-eyed, laidback performances were lazy and lacklustre"

☐ "the naturalism and humour of his acting are truly immortal"

b) Write down three generalisations which the writer makes in this article.

1. ....

2. ....

3. ....

c) How effective is the writer's use of generalisation and counter-argument in this article? MINI-ESSAY QUESTION

Counter Arguments — like Tiddly-Winks in a fight...

Generalisations and counter-arguments are sneaky persuasive techniques that writers use.
You need to be able to spot when a writer has used them **and** discuss how effective they are.

Rhetoric and Bias

Q1 Draw lines to match up each persuasive technique to the sentence which uses it.

a) **rhetorical question**　　　　i) Nothing is more disgusting than a mouldy sandwich.

b) **repetition of words/phrases**　ii) Who on earth would want to eat a mouldy sandwich?

c) **exaggeration**　　　　　　　iii) I hate mould. I hate sandwiches. I really hate mouldy sandwiches.

Q2 Underline whether you think the following texts are biased or unbiased. Explain your answers.

a)
> By far the best hobby for young people is the card game "cribbage". All young people from the ages of eight to eighteen adore playing cribbage. It's easy to learn, doesn't need much equipment and provides hours of fun.

I think the text is **biased / unbiased** because ....

....

....

....

b)
> In Orkney, you can visit the remains of a Neolithic (Stone Age) village called Skara Brae. The village was inhabited about 5000 years ago. You can see the remains of walls, doorways, fireplaces and stone "furniture".

I think the text is **biased / unbiased** because ....

....

....

....

Q3 Read the following extract from a travel brochure and answer the question which follows.

> ### Malliwest Resort Hotels
>
> Everyone daydreams. When you're stuck in the office — dealing with tricky customers, struggling with spreadsheets, drinking tepid tea — can you honestly say you haven't dreamt of lying on a sublime beach in a luxury resort, sipping cocktails and being waited on hand and foot?
>
> At Malliwest Resorts you can make your dreams a reality. Only at Malliwest Resorts can you reserve a private beach so that no one else can see what you look like in your swimming costume. Only at Malliwest Resorts can you order your favourite meal and have it made specially. Only at Malliwest Resorts can you ring room service at 4am and get a polite response!
>
> Malliwest Resorts' top priority is to make sure you have the **holiday of a lifetime**. If you book before 20th June, you'll get 15% off the price of your holiday. Surely this is an offer to fulfil anyone's dreams?

How does the writer use rhetorical language to persuade the reader?

MINI-ESSAY
QUESTION

Section Two — Following an Argument

Headlines, Subheadings and Straplines

Q1   Label this newspaper front page with the correct terms from the box.

byline	subheading	strapline
caption	headline	standfirst

The Grizebeck Guardian

a) ....

Teapot stolen from village hall

Shocking story of theft rocks village

b) ....

c) ....

By our crime reporter, Barry Fanciabrew

Details emerged last night of the teapot theft scandal that has rocked the local area and left residents terrified.

The teapot that has served villagers for a good few months disappeared in the early hours of Monday morning.

Lapsang Souchong
The regular Thursday evening pot of Lapsang Souchong is now in jeopardy and fears are growing that the situation could deteriorate further as police probe claims that a number of saucers "seem to have gone missing lately."

Local residents are now trying to come to terms with the loss and are scratching their heads trying to think what could have happened.

Suspect
Suspicions initially fell on Earl Grey enthusiast Cath Norton, who had earlier been quoted as saying that she "fancied a cuppa".

But Norton denied the claims, pointing out she already owned a really nice brown teapot she'd been given by her mum.

"And anyway," she added, "I've gone off tea lately – I prefer a nice hot chocolate these days, and you can't make that in a pot."

MYSTERY: The missing teapot, which was bought for £7.99 last March (or maybe April)

Borrowing suggestion
The story took a new twist last night as grocer Bob Peasbody remembered something someone had said the other day.

"Actually," he commented, "I think Mavis from down the road said she was borrowing it for a couple of days as her aunt's up for the weekend". He went on to speculate that she would "probably put it back sooner or later."

Opinion from Dave Gribbett: "Let's not worry about it too much – worse things happen, eh?" See pages 10-12.

e) ....

d) ....

f) ....

Q2   For each of the following headlines, write down one language device which makes it effective. Write a brief explanation of how each language device works.

a)   "Ray Runs Riot in Sheldon Showdown"

....

....

b)   "Indian restaurant curries favour from locals"

....

....

c)   "Outrage at massive tax increase"

....

....

Graphics and Captions

Q1   Briefly explain the intended purpose of each graphic and its caption.

a)   (from a newspaper article about population growth)

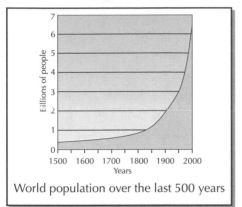

World population over the last 500 years

b)   (from a hotel brochure)

All our rooms are clean, comfortable and luxurious

c)   (from a political leaflet)

Your local council election candidate, Jeff Powell

a) ....

....

....

b) ....

....

....

c) ....

....

....

Q2   Read the following advertisement for the holiday destination of Montserrat. How do the headings, photographs and captions help to achieve the text's purpose?

MINI-ESSAY QUESTION

MONTSERRAT
The Emerald Isle of the Caribbean

Montserrat is a beautiful, lush, green, mountainous island, which Irish settlers named "the Emerald Isle of the Caribbean". Montserrat lies 27 miles south-west of Antigua, in the Eastern Caribbean chain of islands.

Relax on the island's idyllic, secluded beaches

Learn to dive amid beautiful unspoilt coral reefs

The beaches in Montserrat are remarkable in appearance as they have glistening black sand due to the volcanic nature of the island. They are some of the most secluded and unspoilt beaches in the world. For swimming and sunbathing they provide the most calming and leisurely experience available. The beaches also provide incomparable surroundings for diving, snorkelling, and other water sports.

For more information, go to www.visitmontserrat.com

Text Positioning

Q1　How does the use of columns in the following texts add to their effectiveness?

a)

Parrots under threat from pet trade

A British-based conservation organisation has warned that the future of the world's parrots is becoming severely threatened by the international trade for pets.

Thousands of parrots are captured and brought to Europe and North America each year, with many dying during the journey. Neotropical parrots have become one of the most threatened groups of birds in the world, because of international trade and also deforestation of their natural habitats.

This trend is all the more alarming, the organisation says, because until recently parrots have flourished, with numbers on the increase.

....

....

b)

Item	Was	Now	SAVING
Stanford office desk	£149.99	£99.99	33%
McIntyre Classic Dresser	£899.99	£599.99	33%
Brockwell 3-seater sofa	£750.00	£375.00	50%

....

....

Q2　Explain why you think text boxes have been used in the following examples.

a)

Energise, revitalise and relax...
...and work off those extra pounds!

Bring this document to our reception to claim your free 2-week trial voucher (valid until the end of December). You will be entitled to free gym and pool use, exercise classes, social events and loads more!

....

....

b)

Here are just two examples of people who have benefited from the generosity of people like you:

Name: Oscar Luis
Age: 9
Story: Oscar used to live in a tin hut in the barrios of São Paulo. He now has clean water and basic medical services.

Name: Srinitha
Age: 7
Story: Tiny Srinitha used to beg in the train stations of Delhi. Now she lives in a modest but safe apartment with her foster parents.

....

....

Bullet Points, Numbered Lists and Colour

Q1   Explain why the use of bullet points or numbered lists is effective in the following texts.

a)

Flu strikes hard and fast. Symptoms may include:
- fever
- aching all over the body
- headache
- dry cough
- lack of appetite
- extreme tiredness.

Do I look like I want to write about bullet points?

....

....

....

b)

Chocolate cake recipe:
1) Lightly grease and line two 20cm wide, 4cm deep sandwich tins.
2) Pre-heat the oven to 180°C / gas mark 4.
3) Beat together the butter, sugar, eggs, flour, baking powder and cocoa.
4) Divide the mixture evenly between the prepared tins.
5) Bake for about 25 minutes, until risen and rich, dark brown.

....

....

....

Q2   What impression do you think a writer would be aiming for by using the following colours?

a) **red** text in a leaflet about road safety

....

....

b) a **pink** background in an advertisement for children's dolls

....

....

c) a **red**, **white** and **blue** colour scheme in a tabloid supplement about a royal wedding

....

....

"Interesting" is boring...

When you talk about presentational devices it's important you say <u>how</u> they work. It's no good just saying that they make the text more interesting — you have to explain their specific effect.

Font Styles and Formatting

Q1 What impression is created by the following fonts? Explain why you think each font has been used.

a) | Global warming is "worse than previously thought", say Antarctic scientists |

....

....

b) | **Looking for a great day of family fun? Give Franny's Fun Farm a ring!** |

....

....

c) | *Sometimes you need to take a few risks — and don't underestimate your own abilities...* |

....

....

Q2 Describe the effects of formatting in the following extracts.

a) | The failing company's chief executive has awarded himself a pay rise of a **whopping £5000**! |

....

....

b) | *Date:* 15th April *Time:* 7.30pm *Place:* Hartnell Square *Event:* World Peace Rally |

....

....

Q3 Read the text below and then answer the question at the bottom of the page.

If your New Year's resolution to live more healthily hasn't taken off yet, don't panic — here are some of the top "super foods", as recommended by dieticians:
• <u>Carrots</u> provide beta-carotene, which can reduce the risk of stroke.
• <u>Chilli peppers</u> can help to reduce cholesterol and protect DNA against carcinogens.
• <u>Tomatoes</u> stimulate immune functions and may slow degenerative diseases.
• <u>Citrus fruits</u> are an excellent source of vitamin C, which helps your body fight cancers.

Health experts are keen to point out, though, that in addition to a balanced and nutritious diet, a healthy lifestyle must also include regular exercise. A good mixture of aerobic and anaerobic exercise, taken three times a week, is a good general guide.

"Exercise" doesn't have to mean getting up at 5 am every morning and running a half marathon! Something as easy as a brisk <u>30 minute walk</u> every day can make a big contribution to improved health.

What presentational techniques does the writer of this health leaflet use to present her advice?

MINI-ESSAY QUESTION

Descriptive Language

Q1   Define the term "imagery".

....

....

Q2   For each example, identify the descriptive techniques used and say what impression they create.

a)   As soon as I walked into the house, the squalid, unhygienic conditions were impossible to ignore.

....

....

b)   The scruffy youth had a shock of fiery red hair, so spiky that he looked in a permanent state of surprise.

....

....

c)   I remember my first football match so clearly: the sound of the fans as loud as ten jet engines; the emerald green pitch; the buzzing, electric atmosphere. I'll never forget it.

....

....

Q3   Read the text below, then answer the questions in the lovely coloured boxes.

From *Memories of Aldport,* by Geoff Buckley

    I visited the old, ghostly railway station down the road from where I grew up. The grey, rusty bridge seemed to harbour countless memories of days gone by — the thunderous roar of an approaching train echoing down the track like a premonition of an alien invasion.

    The fact that nothing passes under it any more adds to the eerie atmosphere it has now, and the strange sense of so many lives having been lived under it in the past. I would like to take a stroll along its forbidding, overgrown lines — but the combination of an unnecessary barbed wire fence and the dense, strangulating bushes surrounding the sidings sadly make this impossible.

a)   How does the writer of this text feel about the railway station he describes?

b)   What writing techniques are used to describe the station and trains? How effective are they?

Metaphors, Similes and Analogies

Q1 Draw lines to link each term with its correct definition:

a) **metaphor**   An extended comparison where the writer describes exactly how one thing is like another.

b) **simile**   A comparison where the writer says that something is something else.

c) **analogy**   A comparison where the writer says something is similar to something else, often using the words "like" or "as".

Q2 For each phrase, say whether it is a **metaphor**, a **simile** or an **analogy**.

a) | John's as thick as two short planks. | ⇒ ....

b) | Her eyes were X-rays, penetrating my soul. | ⇒ ....

c) | An atom is similar to a solar system, with the electrons circling the nucleus in much the same way as planets orbit a star. | ⇒ ....

d) | Jane was a tower of strength. | ⇒ ....

e) | I was stuck like a lettuce in a teapot. | ⇒ ....

Q3 What impression is created by the following simile? How does it create this impression?

| Jane's efforts to cheer Tom up were as fruitless as the Sahara Desert. |

....

....

....

Q4 How effective is the following metaphor? Explain your answer.

| His face was a snowfield of fear. |

....

....

....

I know the writer quite well — I metaphor times...

Make sure you've got all these terms worked out in your head before the exam. Metaphors, similes and analogies are similar but you need to learn the differences between them.

Section Four — Writing Techniques

Personification, Alliteration and Onomatopoeia

Q1   Fill in the blanks in the following sentences.

a)   .... means repeating the same sound at the start of words in a phrase.

b)   .... means describing something as if it is a person or animal.

c)   .... means a word that sounds like what it is describing.

Q2   For each extract, write down the technique being used and say what effect it creates.

a)   "The computer squawked into life before cheerily informing me I had performed an illegal operation."

....

....

....

b)   "The thumping beats on offer at the venue now are a different world from the Oompah tunes of old."

....

....

....

c)   "Bag a Bargain at Brigson's — Portsmouth's Premier Pig Farm!"

....

....

....

Q3   Read the following extract from a travel book then answer the question that follows.

> The streets of Kuala Lumpur are a labyrinth of lost lanes, back-streets, dead-ends and confusing alleys which double back on themselves. An apparently infinite series of haphazard side streets breaks out from the main street of the Chinatown area like snakes winding across the desert. On every corner hang the pungent but irresistible smells of food stalls offering a cornucopia of exotic cuisines.
>
> The low growl of heavy trucks and buzzing of the thousands of scooters that swarm the streets like bees made my dreams of a bit of peace and quiet ridiculously optimistic. The sticky heat combined with choking exhaust fumes and incessant noise certainly made for a vibrant but less than relaxing atmosphere.

MINI-ESSAY
QUESTION

What writing techniques does the writer of this text use to make his descriptions vivid and effective?

Irony and Sarcasm

Q1   Briefly explain each of the following terms:

a) irony   ....

....

b) sarcasm   ....

....

c) satire   ....

....

Q2   What is the effect of the writer's sarcastic tone in this article about extending pub licensing hours?

> **From *Unhappy Hour* by Jane Green**
>
> Of course, the solution to binge-drinking is perfectly clear: we should keep pubs open all day long. This way, everyone will get bored of the idea of beer and take up knitting instead. I can picture it now: the young louts who terrorise our streets will surely all turn to each other and say, "Do you know what, Jeremy? This drinking lark just isn't the wheeze it used to be when we got cleared out by 11 — I'm seriously considering my life options".

....

....

....

....

....

....

Q3   How does the writer of the following extract use irony to express his opinion?   MINI-ESSAY QUESTION

> **From *Customer Disservice — modern day madness* by Mel Sage**
>
> The other day I had to phone up my insurance company with the horrendously complicated problem of changing my address. After spending 20 thrilling minutes on hold listening to a variety of boy bands performing their hits, I finally got through to the man on whom my lofty ambition rested — Wayne.
>
> However, there was a slight hitch. It seems that, for such a highly skilled telephone operative as young Wayne, a task which to mere mortals may appear simple must be performed with studious precision. Fortunately, his professionalism shone through as he kept me informed that he was having some "technical problems". Which was obviously of great comfort to me, as I watched night time slowly approach and began to revise my plans for what was left of the week.

Technical and Emotive Language

Q1   For each language feature, fill in the box with a **T** if it's used in technical language or an **E** if it's used in emotive language.

a) statistics ☐

b) bias ☐

c) exaggeration ☐

d) jargon ☐

e) strong opinions ☐

f) rhetorical questions ☐

Q2   Find three features of emotive language in the following text, taken from a leaflet published by an environmental group. For each feature, give an example and describe what effect it creates.

> What kind of future do we want to give our children? Do we want them to have fresh air to breathe? Do we want a clean, safe environment they can enjoy and share with their own children?
>
> Or do we want a filthy, barren, concrete planet with nothing left of our once green and pleasant land, where trees are just something fondly recalled by their old, eccentric grandparents?
>
> The answer is surely obvious. Yet if we allow the situation to carry on as it is now, with mass deforestation and overdevelopment in the world's most fragile environments, we're heading for disaster. We must take action now if we have any hopes of avoiding this catastrophe.

1. ....

....

2. ....

....

3. ....

....

Q3   How does the technical language in this extract from an article about climate help the writer get information across effectively to the reader?

> The United Kingdom has a temperate maritime climate, with most lowland areas receiving between 500 and 1000mm of annual precipitation. Annual temperatures are generally between 5 and 15°C, with urban areas up to 5°C warmer than rural areas, due to the urban heat island effect. The south is also warmer than the north, due to higher levels of insolation*.

* Insolation is radiation from the sun that heats the planet.

....

....

....

....

Tabloid Newspaper Language

Q1   Fill in the table below using examples from the following tabloid newspaper article.

Tubby Teddy's "inbred" gag is no laughing matter

Portly TV funny-man Ted Chance has outraged residents of Greenford by ignorantly slamming them all as "inbred yokels who think gurning is great entertainment".

He made the offensive quip at a comedy festival last week and has left the town fuming. Locals have since made it clear there's fat Chance Ted will be welcome in the town from now on.

Local man Paul Drake launched a stinging attack on Chance's comments, saying: "The man's just shown how ignorant he is. *He should stop and think before he opens his big fat mouth.*"

Defence

The "Cheeky Chancer" tried to defend his gag yesterday, claiming it was tongue-in-cheek. He retorted: "I don't think anyone would have thought twice about it if they hadn't been so touchy."

Language type	Example
Biased language	
Emotive language	
Slang	
Nicknames	
Puns	

Q2   Describe how the following extracts from *The Daily Rubbish* try to attract the reader's interest.

a)   Outspoken rebel backbencher Terry Green has once again torn a gaping rift in his party. Terrible Tel has lambasted the under-fire PM for his "criminal disregard for family values".

....

....

b)   *It's time to stand up for common sense!* Join *The Daily Rubbish*'s campaign and together we can put an end to this bureaucratic nonsense.

....

....

c)   Read our exclusive interview with British tennis ace Maria Dunn today, as she tries to smash her reputation for bottling it at Wimbledon next week.

....

....

Structure

Q1   Circle the features that you would usually expect to find in the body text of an article.

summary of the main points

separate paragraphs

bylines

opinions

headlines

specific details

statistics

Q2   The following extracts have all been taken from the same newspaper article. For each one, say whether you think it is from the **introduction**, the **body** of the article, or the **conclusion**. Explain your answers.

a)   Many motorists are in favour of the new trial scheme, seeing it as a simple, common-sense solution that will reduce the all-too-common frustration of traffic jams. But critics are concerned that, when the hard shoulder is being used for normal traffic, there will no longer be a safe place for broken down vehicles to await rescue — despite assurances that there will be regular patrols by towing vehicles to avoid accidents caused by stationary vehicles.

....

....

....

b)   The main issue is whether it can prove these worries wrong and effectively reduce congestion without adding to accident rates. If it can, it is likely to prove much more popular than other methods, such as toll roads, which are often under-used, and building extra lanes, which attracts complaints for environmental reasons. If the scheme proves successful, it could be introduced to motorways up and down the country.

....

....

....

c)   A controversial new scheme to avoid traffic congestion on one of Britain's busiest roads has divided opinion among motorists and road safety groups. The strategy, on trial from this week, allows drivers to use the hard shoulder when the amount of traffic is highest. The hard shoulder will continue to be used only for breakdowns at less busy times, with motorway signs to tell motorists when they can be used.

....

....

....

Every bit of the article is important

Although they contain less information than the body text, the introduction and conclusion are very important. The intro gets the reader's interest, and the conclusion is what will stick in their mind.

P.E.E.

Q1 In an exam answer, which of the following could you **not** use as an example to back up a point? Circle the correct answer.

   a) A quote from the text.   c) Your opinion of the text.

   b) A fact or statistic from the text.   d) A description of the presentation of the text.

Q2 Read the following exam answers. Tick the answers which use the P.E.E. technique (Point, Example, Explanation).

a)   The writer uses similes to make his description of Kidston's motor racing more vivid. For example, he describes Kidston's Bentley as being "like a cheetah". This shows how powerful and fast Kidston's car was.

b)   The writer says the racing driver Glen Kidston was glamorous and charismatic. He had an affair with the young Barbara Cartland. In 1931, he died tragically in a plane crash in the Drakensberg Mountains.

c)   The writer uses the headline of the magazine article to capture readers' attention. It describes Glen Kidston as "Britain's Forgotten Hero". This sounds glamorous and mysterious and would intrigue readers.

☐   ☐   ☐

Q3 Read the following extract from a tourist information sheet and answer the question which follows.

> <u>Avebury Visitor Centre: Information Sheet 5</u>
> **West Kennet Long Barrow**
>
> West Kennet Long Barrow is an ancient chambered tomb near Avebury. There are five chambers (rooms) in the tomb. It is safe to go inside the tomb to look at the chambers. When the tomb was excavated, different types of skeleton were found in each chamber:
> • Male adult skeletons were found in the main chamber, opposite the entrance.
> • Children's skeletons were found in the chamber to the left of the entrance.
> • The skeletons of elderly people were found in the chamber to the right of the entrance.
> • A mixture of male and female adult skeletons were found in the two other chambers.

Explain how the writer has used a presentational device to make the text more effective. Use the P.E.E. framework below to help you answer the question.

Point ....

....

Example ....

....

Explanation ....

....

....

So much better than freestyle waffling...

P.E.E. gives you a framework for answering exam questions well. For higher mark questions, you'll have to make several points — and back up each one with examples and explanations.

Writing in Paragraphs

Q1   Circle the words and phrases which would be useful for linking paragraphs together.

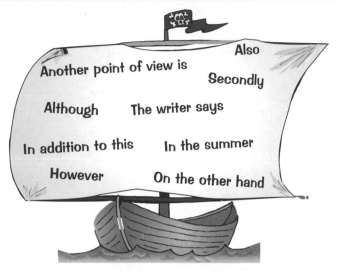

Also

Another point of view is

Secondly

Although   The writer says

In addition to this   In the summer

However   On the other hand

Q2   Read the following exam answers. The student hasn't linked their paragraphs together well. Rewrite the exam answers (a-d), so that the paragraphs are linked smoothly together.

You'll need to write your answers to this question on separate paper.

a)   The writer uses several presentational devices to make the article more effective. One example is the headline which is in a large, bold font. This grabs the reader's attention immediately when they see the article.

    The background colour of the article is grey. This emphasises the sombre tone of the article. Muted colours like grey are associated with serious subjects.

b)   The writer uses linguistic devices to make her argument more persuasive. Firstly, she uses the rhetorical question "Who would want an axe-murderer living next door?" to encourage the reader to identify with her point of view.

    The writer uses a metaphor to describe her opinion: "this situation is a slippery eel which might twist out of our grasp". This creates a vivid image of the difficulty of the situation.

c)   The first text argues in favour of school uniforms. For example, it describes them as "a symbol of unity and school identity" which implies a traditional, positive viewpoint.

    The second text argues against school uniforms. It describes them as "a fashion disaster" and "an embarrassment to pupils". This suggests a very negative opinion.

d)   The book extract is aimed at an audience of primary school children. It includes simple pictures to explain how to use a camera. This makes it easy for children to understand.

    The magazine article is aimed at adults who are interested in photography. It uses technical vocabulary such as "developer" and "focus" which shows it's written for photography enthusiasts.

Q3   Rewrite the following answer. Break it down into three paragraphs and add appropriate words or phrases to make the paragraphs link smoothly together. You will need to use your own paper for this question.

The extract from the biography argues that Orson Welles' career was a "magnificent failure". It points to the fact that his greatest achievement 'Citizen Kane' was made before the age of thirty, and that he ended his career "ignominiously" narrating adverts. The magazine article argues that Orson Welles was a wonderful director and actor throughout his career. It suggests that people like the "myth" of Orson Welles' fall from grace and ignore his later achievements. It describes his "iconic" cameo in 'The Third Man' and his 1958 film 'Touch of Evil' as "neglected high points". The third text, the interview with Orson Welles, shows that he himself had an ambivalent attitude towards his career and achievements. The interviewer describes him as "fiercely proud" of his films, but also "insecure beneath the bravado".

Reading with Insight

Q1   Draw lines to match up each sentence (a-d) with the type of tone it conveys (i-iv).

a)   I was disgusted by the badly researched, shabby journalism displayed by your newspaper's coverage of the event.

b)   The MP Gareth Soames visited the County Hospital on Thursday 11th December to open a new ward.

c)   Gary Barlow's dancing drew gasps of wonder from the crowd — the rumours were true, he really had improved!

d)   There's nothing I love more than queueing in a really long traffic jam on a boiling hot day — it's fantastic.

i) **light-hearted tone**

ii) **sarcastic tone**

iii) **serious tone**

iv) **angry tone**

Q2   Read the following text and answer the questions which follow.

> The films Alfred Hitchcock made in the 1950s and 1960s contain tantalising glimpses of greatness. Iconic images from these films have entered the popular consciousness, for example Janet Leigh screaming in the shower in 'Psycho'.
>
> However, when looking at Hitchcock's career as a whole, it is his earlier films from the 1930s and 1940s which still delight. Early features like 'The 39 Steps' and 'The Lady Vanishes' have a wonderful humour, paciness and lightness of touch. In contrast, his later films, even classics like 'Vertigo' and 'The Birds', are often leaden in their pace and tone.
>
> One reason for the change in quality of Hitchcock's films was the way he started to be treated as a prestigious, "auteur" director as he got older. Younger film directors like François Truffaut revered him. This swelled Hitchcock's already substantial ego, and contributed to an increasingly turgid, self-conscious style of film-making. Stories from the 1950s and 1960s about his bullying, possessive attitude towards young actresses like Tippi Hedren, also raise doubts about his professionalism in his later years.
>
> So my advice is: settle down on the sofa to watch some of those early, off-the-cuff, Hitchcock masterpieces — and leave the later "classics" for nerdy film students.

a)   Pick out words and phrases from the text to complete the table below.

Question 2
take 2

Words and phrases which imply the writer dislikes Hitchcock's later films	Words and phrases which imply the writer likes Hitchcock's early films	Words and phrases which imply the writer dislikes Hitchcock as a person
1.	1.	1.
2.	2.	2.

b)   How does the tone of the text change in the last paragraph?

....

....

....

c)   In this text, the writer describes his enthusiasm for Alfred Hitchcock's early films. Describe something you feel enthusiastic about — and explain how this helps you understand the writer's feelings.

....

....

....

Comparing Texts

Q1   Read the following two texts and answer the questions which follow.

Linda's Problem Page — answers your most embarrassing problems!!!

I farted in front of him!
Dear Linda,
There's a boy at school I really like. He sat next to me in a Maths lesson and I was really excited cos I thought he might fancy me. But I farted and he hasn't talked to me since. What can I do? Love Zoe xxxxxx

Linda says....
Hi Zoe,
Oops! How embarrassing! Don't worry though. Silly moments like this happen to all of us. If this boy really likes you, he won't let one fart get in the way of a relationship. My advice is: be confident, and go and talk to him next time you see him. You'll both soon forget all about it. Good luck! Linda.

Write to Linda c/o 'Girl!' magazine, PO Box 5058

Personal Financial Advice: Case Study

Case Study: Ms Barber, 35, single, no dependants
Salary: £18,000 per annum
Savings: £14,500 in an ISA, 3.5% interest
Pension: Contributes 8% of her salary to a private stakeholder pension.
Property: 1 bed flat, mortgage £290/month.
Debt: Credit card debt £2100, 9% APR

The Daily Missive's financial advisor, Greg Smith writes Ms Barber should pay off her credit card debt using part of her ISA savings. She's currently paying more interest on her credit card debt than she is earning on her ISA.

Secondly, Ms Barber should find out whether her employer would be prepared to make contributions to her pension, which would improve her pension fund.

Finally, Ms Barber should move her ISA to a different bank or building society. 3.5% isn't a competitive rate of interest for an ISA. She should aim for 4.5%.

a)   Complete the following table with notes about the two texts.

	Linda's Problem Page	Personal Financial Advice
Audience of text		
Purpose of text		
Tone of text		
Main language devices used		
Main presentational devices used		

b)   Compare how each text uses language and presentational devices.

MINI-ESSAY QUESTION

Tone is informal — when he's on holiday with Cherie...

You're rattling through the book now — only the exam section left to go. Don't worry about that — it might look like a tiger, but it's really just a harmless tabby cat. Ahh.

Sample Exam — Questions

In this section, <u>you</u> get to be the <u>examiner</u>. You'll look at some students' answers to exam questions and <u>decide what marks</u> they should get. It'll help you understand what examiners are looking for — which will improve the quality of your own answers. Here's how it works:

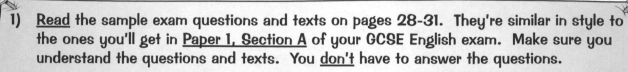

1) <u>Read</u> the sample exam questions and texts on pages 28-31. They're similar in style to the ones you'll get in <u>Paper 1, Section A</u> of your GCSE English exam. Make sure you understand the questions and texts. You <u>don't</u> have to answer the questions.

2) Then on pages 32-39 there are <u>mark schemes</u> explaining <u>how to mark</u> each question. And there are some <u>student answers</u> which you have to mark.

Here are the sample exam questions. Remember — <u>this time</u>, you don't have to answer the questions. Phew.

---

1   Read **Item A**, an advertisement for the medical charity Médecins Sans Frontières.

(a)   How does the photograph help persuade the reader to make a donation to the charity?

(3 marks)

(b)   How effective is the advertisement in using facts and opinions to persuade the reader?

(8 marks)

2   Read **Item B**, the article called *Voluntary work abroad* from the British Government website.

(a)   What are the main points **Item B** makes to encourage readers to take part in voluntary work abroad?

(6 marks)

(b)   Now look at **both** texts and compare them.

Compare:

• the purposes of the texts
• what they say about working abroad
• the language used

(10 marks)

And tonight Matthew — I will be The Examiner...

Enjoy being an examiner while you can. Cherish the feeling of power... Buy a red pen... On p.40 your examiner status will be taken away and you'll have to answer the questions again. Drat.

Sample Exam — Item A

Here's Item A for the exam on page 28. It's an advert for the medical charity Médecins Sans Frontières (MSF). Give it a read through.

EYEWITNESS

© Kadir van Lohuizen

Meriel Rosser from the UK has volunteered for MSF in many countries around the world, but she just can't help returning to Sudan. Here she describes the ongoing crisis in Darfur. Although media coverage of the region has declined, the situation has still not improved for the millions of people caught up in the conflict there.

MSF volunteer Meriel Rosser delivers a message from the frontline.

"It is 2.20 am and 34 degrees C... Welcome to Khartoum!" I seem to be attached to a piece of elastic that keeps bouncing me back to Sudan since my first stint here some three years ago. Then I was in charge of MSF's work treating the deadly disease kala azar (also know as visceral leishmaniasis) in Gedaref state in the east of the country.

Now I'm in the west in Darfur, where the fighting that has been going on here over the last three years has had terrible consequences for the people.

I'm based in Muhajariya, a heartland of the Sudan Liberation Army. MSF is trying to meet some of the huge needs that have arisen because people have fled their homes and because basic necessities like water and sanitation and especially medical services are so limited. During the time we have worked in Darfur we have been providing nutritional support to malnourished children and running a field hospital carrying out surgery for Caesarean sections, as well as injuries related to the ongoing violence, such as gunshot wounds. We also run clinics where we provide primary health care and see people affected by diarrhoea, fever and, at the moment, a lot of malaria.

Darfur is a tough place to work, and the medical needs remain enormous. Violence against civilians continues and people are forced to flee their homes repeatedly. Getting enough food and other humanitarian support is a continuous battle.

We have dealt with births, deaths (always too many, but we know there are many more we save), reports of

Dengue fever in the next state, rabies cases around Darfur... the challenges are endless. Although it's not easy, I do sometimes look around and think that I'm lucky to be in a position to experience this – the beautiful smiling faces of children, the graceful herders on their camels and the waves from people going about their everyday business. And I'm even luckier to be part of an organisation that can really do something to help the most vulnerable.

We are able to do that because people like you support our work. You allow us to react quickly and independently. I am continually amazed at just how much we can do thanks to you.

> **66** *Just because Darfur is not in the news as much as it was a year or so ago does not mean that the situation for individuals living the nightmare has improved at all.* **99**
> Meriel Rosser, MSF volunteer, Darfur, Sudan

(Above image) April 4, 2006: Kalma camp, Darfur, women patiently wait to be seen by an MSF doctor. The health of women is a particular concern because they have to shoulder the burden of taking care of huge families without resources or support. This leaves many exhausted and vulnerable to illness.

MEDECINS SANS FRONTIERES

ENGLISH CHARITY REGISTRATION NUMBER 1026588

To help MSF with a monthly donation, please go to www.uk.msf.org/support EMC2

Sample Exam — Item B

And here's Item B for the exam on page 28. It's an article from the British Government website.

Voluntary work abroad

Ever wanted to combine travelling with making a difference? Through volunteering abroad you could do both. Wherever your skills and experience lie and whatever your interests, there is likely to be a project suited to you.

From animal and environmental projects to helping rebuild communities that have been destroyed by an earthquake, giving even a few weeks of your time will bring real benefits to the area and the people that live there. Through volunteering in another country you can also broaden your horizons, learn about a different culture and make new friends.

Volunteers come from all walks of life including homeworkers, students during a gap year, teachers, engineers, health workers, scientists and government officers.

International experience, in the workplace or as a volunteer, also adds another interesting dimension to your CV and can make your job or promotion application stand out.

Volunteering opportunities on offer

Organisations like the British Council, Voluntary Services Overseas (VSO) and charities with international units can help you make a decision about volunteering abroad and find the right project for you. The Year Out Group also has information on a range of volunteering opportunities.

take time to find a project that suits you

The British Council's Connect Youth offers programmes ranging from group exchanges to individual voluntary service, designed to give young people an international experience.

The VSO is an international development charity, which tries to match people's skills and professional background to the need for volunteers across the world. The ages of its volunteers range from 17 to 75.

If there is a particular charity or voluntary organisation you would like to help, contact it to find out if it needs any volunteers to work overseas.

The first volunteering project you find is not necessarily going to be ideally suited to you, but it is worth looking until you discover something you would feel comfortable doing.

Sample Exam — Item B

Talk to the organisers of the volunteer programme about any concerns and check what safety measures are in place, as well as what would happen if you had to return to the UK earlier than you had expected or you find the project is not for you.

Taking a career break from your job

If you are in paid employment, find out how taking a career break or secondment to volunteer abroad would affect your work contract, health cover, pension and national insurance contributions, as well as your continued service.

Some employers will have a policy to encourage their staff to take part in volunteering or see a community project they are sponsoring abroad. Others may consider counting your volunteering period as extended leave without pay or as a secondment - this could be helpful if you are considering volunteering abroad for a long period.

If you expect to return to your job at the end of your volunteering period, give your employer your contact details and the name of the organisation you are volunteering through in case they need to contact you urgently or update you about developments in the firm.

Before you go

Make sure you have the vaccinations you need for the country and check if there is any travel safety advice from the Foreign and Commonwealth Office.

You will need a valid passport to cover the entire period you will be overseas. It is also worth finding out the contact details and location of the British Consul in the country where you will be working (see the related links on this page).

The organisation you will be working through may have travel and health insurance to cover you while you are abroad. Check what you are covered for and if you need to take out any additional policies.

While you are away, try and keep regular contact with the charity or organisation you are volunteering through and make sure they know where to find you in case of an emergency. This will help you find out about any changes in the country that may affect your safety or health. If you are concerned about the situation in a country, keep in contact with the British consul in the area.

Wherever you choose to volunteer, enjoy the experience as it can be fun as well as rewarding.

www.direct.gov.uk © Crown Copyright

Mark Scheme — Question 1 (a)

This page gives you <u>advice and a mark scheme</u> for marking question 1 (a) of the sample exam. Read this information and digest it. Then you'll be ready for marking the student answers on p.33.

Question 1 (a) is worth 3 marks so it only needs a short answer

1) One or two good, well-explained points would be enough to answer this question well.

2) Even if a student wrote a brilliant, ten-page essay for their answer, they could still only get 3 marks.

Paul was thirty years old and had written five books about the MSF photograph before he realised the question was only worth 3 marks.

Look for good points like these when you're marking

If a student's written good points like these in their answer, they're on track for a good mark...

- The photograph shows a long queue of women waiting to be seen by the MSF doctor. This emphasises the demand for the charity's work and suggests that more doctors are needed, which might persuade readers to donate money.
- The photograph shows an MSF doctor at work, treating a patient. This emphasises how practical and useful the charity's work is, which might persuade readers to donate.

There are plenty of other good points that could get marks — these are just suggestions.

Use this mark scheme to mark question 1 (a)

Look at the table below to see what an answer needs to be like to get each mark. When you're marking an answer, look at this table and work out which descriptions <u>fit the answer best</u> — that's the mark you should give.

Number of marks	What's been written	How it's written	How the answer's put together
0	Nothing relevant to the question written.	Nothing relevant to the question written.	Nothing relevant to the question written.
1	Some attempt to answer the question. Some description of the photograph.	Confusingly written.	Unstructured answer. Information isn't in a clear or logical order.
2	Clear attempt to answer the question. Backs up answer using detail from text.	Writing is generally clear — though may be confusing in places.	Structured answer. Information is in a fairly clear, logical order.
3	Detailed answer to the question. Clearly explains persuasive effect of photograph.	Clearly and thoughtfully written.	Well-structured answer. Shapes material into a clear, logical order.

A good mark — like that nice lad from Take That...

The mark scheme table might look a bit scary at first — but give it a read through and you'll see it's common sense really. The better the answer, the better the mark. It ain't rocket science.

Sample Answers — Question 1 (a)

Now it's your turn to be the examiner. This can be tricky but it's really useful if you can do it.

1) Make sure you've read the advice and mark scheme on page 32.
2) Use the mark scheme to mark the answers to question 1 (a) below.
3) Explain how you've decided on the marks in the lines below the answers.
4) The first one's been done for you to show you what to do.

Write notes around the answer — that's what the real examiners do.

> 1 (a) How does the photograph help persuade the reader to make a donation to the charity?
>
> (3 marks)

Answer 1

Q1 (a) The photograph shows one of the charity's volunteers helping a patient. This shows the good work the charity does and might make readers think more about the work it does.

This answer gets [2] marks out of 3 because it makes a good, simple point about the photograph and tries to link this to the persuasive purpose of the text. The answer isn't very clear at the end though and so probably doesn't deserve the full 3 marks.

Answer 2

Q1 (a) It shows a doctor for the charity treating some patients. The photo is quite big and takes up lots of room.

This answer gets [ ] marks out of 3 because ....

Answer 3

Q1 (a) The photograph shows one of the charity's doctors helping a patient, with a long queue of people waiting for his attention. This emphasises the practical nature and usefulness of the charity's work, and would help to persuade readers to donate to the charity.

This answer gets [ ] marks out of 3 because ....

Section Six — Sample Exam

Mark Scheme — Question 1 (b)

Here's advice and a mark scheme for marking question 1 (b). Read all this info through — then you'll be prepared for marking the sample student answers on the next page.

Question 1 (b) is worth 8 marks so it needs a longer answer

1) A good answer would need <u>three or four points</u> — backed up with examples and explanations.

2) The answer needs to be <u>balanced</u> (discussing both facts and opinions) to get all the marks.

Look for good points like these when you're marking

These are the kinds of points you'd find in a good answer to the question...

- The advert includes a long quote from a volunteer. This describes both the overall facts of the situation ("violence against civilians continues") and the volunteer's opinions ("I am continually amazed at just how much we can do"). These combine to persuade the reader to donate.

- The opinions of the volunteer are very positive and supportive about the work of the charity. Strong statements like "I'm even luckier to be part of an organisation which can really do something" help to persuade the reader that it's a good charity and worth supporting.

- The advert uses facts to describe the work of the charity. It mentions "providing nutritional support to malnourished children and running a field hospital". These examples emphasise the good work the charity is doing, and illustrate what donated money would be used for.

- The volunteer quoted in the advert has first hand experience of working for MSF in a conflict zone. This means her opinions are more persuasive because she is talking as an expert.

Mark question 1 (b) like this

Here's the mark scheme table for question 1 (b). It's bigger than a baboon's bottom.

Number of marks	What's been written	How it's written	How the answer's put together
0	Nothing relevant to the question written.	Nothing relevant to the question written.	Nothing relevant to the question written.
1	Not much written. Some basic attempt to answer question.	Written in a confusing way. Might copy out sections of the text (copying, not quoting).	Unstructured answer — information is in no obvious order.
2-3	Might only discuss fact or opinion — not both. Mentions one or two important points.	Writing is unclear in places Might copy out sections of the text.	Points loosely organised.
4-5	Writes about use of both fact and opinion — though answer may not be balanced. Mentions purpose of advert.	Quite clearly written and mostly easy to follow. Mainly written in own words.	Clear structure that is generally kept to, with most points linked together.
6-7	Writes about use of both fact and opinion in detail and links this clearly to persuasive purpose of the text. Uses appropriate examples to back up points.	Well written, clear explanations. Uses own words.	Clearly structured answer with points neatly linked together.
8	Detailed, convincing points, discussing the effectiveness of fact and opinion in persuading the reader. Good selection of examples to back up points.	Clearly and confidently written, with accurate use of technical terms.	Well organised answer that flows well and is easy to follow.

Sample Answers — Question 1 (b)

Now it's time to have a go at marking answers to question 1 (b). Don't be too merciless...

1) Read the mark scheme on page 34.
2) Use this mark scheme to <u>mark</u> the answers below to question 1 (b).
3) Then <u>explain</u> why you gave those marks in the lines below the answers.

It's how you explain your marking that's the important bit.

> 1   (b)   How effective is the advertisement in using facts and opinions to persuade the reader?
>
> (8 marks)

Answer 1

Q1 (b)   The advertisement uses facts to persuade the reader to support the charity. It gives factual examples of the work the charity does, such as "providing nutritional support to malnourished children and running a field hospital". It also says they help with surgery for Caesarean sections, as well as injuries related to the ongoing violence. This helps to show readers how useful the charity's work is and might make them donate money.

This answer gets ☐ marks out of 8 because ....

....

....

....

....

Answer 2

Q1 (b)   The advertisement uses facts to give evidence of the charity's good work, for example "providing nutritional support to malnourished children". This is effective in persuading the reader that it is a good charity to support.

The advertisement also uses opinions to help persuade the reader. For example, it uses a lengthy quote from an MSF volunteer who is very positive about the charity. For example, she is quoted as saying, "I'm even luckier to be part of an organisation that can really do something to help".

This answer gets ☐ marks out of 8 because ....

....

....

....

....

Sampler answers — cross stitched very slowly...

How are you finding being the examiner? If you really like it, you could always do a degree in English, then a **PGCE** teacher qualification and then apply to be one for real... Take a while though.

Mark Scheme — Question 2 (a)

Hopefully you'll be getting the hang of it by now. Read through the advice and mark scheme on this page, then mark the answers on p.37.

Question 2 (a) is trickier than it looks

1) With this type of question, it's important to explain what the text is saying <u>in your own words</u>. Short quotes are all right, but you shouldn't just copy out large chunks of the text.

2) The question's testing the ability to <u>follow what a writer is saying</u> and pick out the main points.

Pointy hats, claws, sabres, horns and teeth get 0 marks.

Look for good points like these when you're marking

- The writer says that voluntary work abroad is a way of combining travel with "making a difference" through charity work.

- The article emphasises that there is a wide variety of voluntary work abroad available — which means there will be something to suit everyone, whatever their skills.

- The article says that volunteers come from many different backgrounds. This encourages readers to feel that they could also be a volunteer.

- The writer implies that volunteering abroad is a valuable learning experience. Volunteers learn about different cultures which will "broaden" their horizons.

- The article emphasises that it is often possible to take a career break from a job in order to experience volunteering. It also says that experience of voluntary work abroad can improve career prospects when applying for a new job or promotion.

- The article says that volunteering abroad is a good way to make new friends. The end of the article emphasises that volunteering should be an enjoyable and "fun" experience.

Remember — these are just suggestions.

Mark question 2 (a) like this

The table below describes what an answer needs to be like to get each mark.

Number of marks	What's been written	How it's written	How the answer's put together
0	Nothing relevant to the question written.	Nothing relevant to the question written.	Nothing relevant to the question written.
1	Little detail and not much relevant information.	Confusingly written. May have copied out sections of the text.	Unstructured answer. Information isn't in clear or logical order.
2	A few basic points but not all of them relevant and not much detail.	Writing isn't very clear. May have copied parts of text.	No clear structure.
3	Several points but not in much detail	Mostly explains points in own words. Writing unclear in places.	Loose structure but some points don't fit in with it.
4	Picks out most of the main points made by text. Shows fairly good understanding of text.	Mostly written in own words with fairly clear descriptions of the main points.	Fairly clear structure (e.g. new paragraph for each point, and follows order points appear in text).
5	Clear explanations of the writer's main points. Shows good understanding of the text.	Written in own words. Clear and accurate explanations of the main points of the text.	Good, clear structure.
6	Very clear explanations of the main points of the text. Shows detailed understanding of the text.	Clear, confident explanations of the main points the text uses to encourage readers to volunteer.	Good, clear structure with paragraphs linked smoothly together.

Sample Answers — Question 2 (a)

More marking for you to do on this page. Remember to write "v.g." on the good answers...

1) Read the mark scheme on page 36.

2) Use this mark scheme to <u>mark</u> these answers to question 2 (a).

3) Then <u>explain</u> why you gave those marks in the lines below the answers.

> 2   (a)   What are the main points **Item B** makes to encourage readers to take part in voluntary work abroad?
>
> (6 marks)

Answer 1

Q2(a)   My uncle is a doctor and he did a VSO trip four years ago. He really enjoyed the experience and recommended it. He thought that working abroad could really broaden your skills.

This answer gets ☐ marks out of 6 because ....

....

....

....

Answer 2

Q2(a)   The article says that wherever your skills and experience lie and whatever your interests, there will be a project suited to you. It says working abroad will "broaden your horizons". It says you can have fun and make new friends.

This answer gets ☐ marks out of 6 because ....

....

....

....

Answer 3

Q2(a)   Firstly, the article makes the point that there are a broad range of opportunities for working abroad available. It claims that whatever a reader's background and skills, there is likely to be a project suitable for them. It emphasises that "volunteers come from all walks of life" to encourage all readers to feel that they could become involved.

Secondly, the article argues that volunteering abroad is a "fun" and rewarding experience. It describes how volunteering can "broaden your horizons", enabling you to learn about a different country and make new friends. By emphasising the benefits of volunteering abroad, the article encourages readers to try it.

This answer gets ☐ marks out of 6 because ....

....

....

....

Mark Scheme — Question 2 (b)

This is the last question on the exam paper — and the <u>hardest</u>. Read through this page to find out what a good answer needs to be like.

Question 2 (b) is worth a whopping 10 marks

1) This question needs a long and <u>detailed</u> answer to get all 10 marks.

2) Good answers need to cover <u>all three</u> bullet points.

3) It's a <u>comparing</u> question — so answers <u>have to compare</u> the texts to do well. It's not enough to write about both texts separately — the answer has to discuss <u>similarities</u> and <u>differences</u>.

The similarities were obvious.

Look for good points like these when you're marking

- The purpose of the MSF advert is to persuade the reader to "help MSF with a monthly donation". This purpose is made clear in the text at the bottom of the page. This text is in a box and in a larger font to make it stand out. The purpose of Item B, on the other hand, is both to advise and persuade. It gives advice about volunteering abroad, for example under the subheading "Before you go". However, it also persuades the reader to volunteer, by emphasising the benefits, for example saying "you can also broaden your horizons."

- The MSF advert portrays working abroad as a worthwhile but difficult challenge. A metaphor is used to describe the work as "a continuous battle" which emphasises how hard it is. In contrast, Item B emphasises positive points about working abroad to encourage people to volunteer, for example saying that it will be "fun" and that you can "make new friends".

- The MSF advert includes a long quote from a volunteer which has a personal, informal tone, e.g. "And I'm even luckier". This colloquial language makes it sound as if the volunteer is talking to the reader and adds to the persuasive effect. Item B also has a fairly informal, friendly tone. For example, it addresses the reader as "you" which makes the advice sound like it's aimed directly at the reader.

Mark question 2(b) like this

Number of marks	What's been written	How it's written	How the answer's put together
0	Nothing relevant to the question written.	Nothing relevant to the question written.	Nothing relevant to the question written.
1	Not much written. Some basic attempt to answer question.	Written in a confusing way.	Unstructured answer — information is in no obvious order.
2-3	A few brief points. Only covers one or two of the bullet points. Might not directly compare texts.	Writing isn't very clear or easy to follow.	Very little structure with few links between points.
4-5	Covers at least two of the bullet points. Some attempt to compare texts.	Quite clearly written and mostly easy to follow.	Points loosely organised into basic structure.
6-7	All three bullet points covered, in varying amounts of detail. Evidence from texts used to back up some points.	Well written, with clear explanations.	Clear structure that is generally kept to, with most points linked.
8-9	All three bullet points covered in equal detail with good selection of examples to back up points.	Clearly and confidently written, with accurate use of technical terms.	Clearly structured answer with points neatly linked together.
10	Detailed and thoughtful comparisons, covering all three bullet points in depth with well chosen evidence.	Stylishly written with a confident tone and convincing use of technical terms.	Clear, consistent structure that flows well and is easy to follow.

Sample Answers — Question 2 (b)

This is your final page of marking. Then everything's back to normal in section 7.

1) Read the mark scheme and advice on page 38.

2) Use this mark scheme to <u>mark</u> these answers to question 2 (b).

3) Then <u>explain</u> why you gave those marks in the lines below the answers.

> 2   (b)   Now look at **both** texts and compare them.
>
>   Compare:
> - the purposes of the texts
> - what they say about working abroad
> - the language used   (10 marks)

Answer 1

Q2 (b)   The first text is about trying to persuade the reader and the second text is about trying to advise them. The first text is about trying to get people to donate money. Therefore it talks about how awful conditions are in Sudan. It says it's "tough" working there. The second text advises people about going abroad to do volunteering. It mostly says good things about working abroad. It says that it can "broaden your horizons" and it's "fun".

This answer gets ☐ marks out of 10 because ....

....

....

....

....

Answer 2

Q2 (b)   The purpose of the charity advert is to persuade readers "to help MSF with a monthly donation". The purpose of the 'Voluntary work abroad' article, on the other hand, is to advise readers about working abroad. It discusses the opportunities available, career breaks and what to think about "before you go".

     The charity advert includes a message from one of its volunteers working in the Sudan. Their work is described as "tough" and a "continuous battle". This emphasises the important, difficult work done by the charity. In contrast, the article mainly describes the benefits of working abroad, for example, meeting new friends and learning about new cultures.

     The language used by both the article and the advert are fairly informal. The advert uses a quote from a volunteer; this uses the first person and some colloquial language, for example, "I'm even luckier". The article addresses the reader as "you" and has a friendly tone.

This answer gets ☐ marks out of 10 because ....

....

....

....

....

Practice Exam — Questions

Here are some practice exam questions for 'Reading non-fiction and media texts'. They're similar in style to the ones you'll get in <u>Paper 1, Section A</u> of your GCSE English exam.

To make it more like the real exam, do <u>all the questions</u> in one go, and give yourself <u>one hour</u> to answer them. Try to use everything you've learnt so far about what makes a good exam answer...

---

1   Read **Item A**, the article *Cartoon duo play cat and mouse with PC police*.

     (a)   What methods does **Item A** use to entertain the reader?

                                                           (8 marks)

     (b)   Suggest what the writer's opinion of the Tom and Jerry smoking issue is in **Item A**. Explain how this is implied in the text.

                                                            (3 marks)

2   Read **Item B**, an extract from the factsheet *Stopping smoking: The benefits and aids to quitting* from the ASH website.

     (a)   What are the main points **Item B** makes to support the idea that many smokers have the desire to stop smoking?

                                                            (4 marks)

     (b)   How do the presentational devices used in **Item B** help it to achieve its purpose?

                                                            (6 marks)

     (c)   Now look at **both** texts. Compare the language used in **Item A** and **Item B**.

                                                            (6 marks)

Practice Exam — Item A

Here's the first text to go with the practice exam questions on page 40. It's an article from 'The Times' newspaper.

Cartoon duo play cat and mouse with PC police

Tom and Jerry* are in trouble for lighting up in front of children, writes **Alan Hamilton**

BOGIE* puffed on *The African Queen,* Eastwood chewed his cheroot* through all those spaghetti westerns, and even Gandalf the Wizard lights up his pipe in *The Lord of the Rings.* The recent film about Ed Murrow and Senator Joe McCarthy, *Good Night, and Good Luck,* set in the Fifties, was shot in a positive fug of cigarette smoke.

Now a far more politically incorrect cinematic moment has been brought to the attention of Ofcom, the broadcasting watchdog: Tom has been smoking in front of Jerry.

People with no sense of humour occasionally complain at the violence on the classic Hanna-Barbera cat-and-mouse cartoon series, which has delighted children of all ages since the 1940s.

Feline tobacco use was spotted by a viewer in two *Tom and Jerry* episodes shown regularly on Boomerang, a children's cartoon channel owned by Ted Turner's CNN organisation.

The offending cartoons are *Tennis Chumps* and *Texas Tom.* In the former, Tom's opponent in a match is seen drawing on a large cigar. In the latter, Tom tries to impress a female cat by rolling a cigarette, lighting it and smoking it, all with one hand. It is a skill which, in this country at least, sometimes raises suspicions that the performer picked up the trick behind bars.

After the complaint Turner conducted a review of its *Tom and Jerry* library to assess any smoking scenes and the context in which they appear.

Cecilia Persson, a vice-president of Turner Broadcasting, said yesterday that it had "a responsibility to create a safe place for kids to watch TV".

The channel had edited out two scenes where smoking could be deemed to be glamorised, and would review its library of cartoons to remove any other glamorising references to smoking. Turner has told Ofcom, however, that removing all scenes of smoking in cartoons "might adversely affect the value of the animation".

Ofcom's broadcast code states that smoking must not be featured in programmes made primarily for children unless there is strong editorial justification, and it must not be condoned*, encouraged or glamorised before the watershed*.

The watchdog acknowledged that most *Tom and Jerry* cartoons were made in an era* when smoking was acceptable, and it usually appeared "in a stylised manner and is frequently not condoned".

A spokesman for the BBC said that whatever happened to *Tom and Jerry* would also apply to that most habitual of all cartoon smokers, Popeye, who is rarely seen without his trademark corncob pipe.

"I yam what I yam what I yam," said Popeye. Ah, you haven't met Ofcom, then?

© *The Times London, 22nd August 2006*

* Tom and Jerry = cartoon characters of a cat and mouse who fight each other
* Bogie = Humphrey Bogart, a film star in the 1940s and 1950s
* cheroot = a cigar cut square at both ends
* condoned = treated as acceptable
* watershed = a time in television schedules (9pm on standard television) before which television programmes which contain adult content are not allowed to be shown.
* era = time period

Practice Exam — Item B

Here's the second text for the exam questions on page 40. It's a factsheet from the website of the anti-smoking charity ASH (Action on Smoking and Health).

factsheet no:11

Stopping smoking: The benefits and aids to quitting

Action on Smoking and Health — November 2005

The desire to stop smoking

Many smokers continue smoking not through free choice but because they are addicted to the nicotine in cigarettes. A report by the Royal College of Physicians found that nicotine complied with the established criteria for defining an addictive substance. The report states: "On present evidence, it is reasonable to conclude that nicotine delivered through tobacco smoke should be regarded as an addictive drug, and tobacco use as the means of nicotine self-administration."[1]

Surveys have consistently shown that at least 70% of adult smokers would like to stop smoking and of those who express a desire to quit, more than a third are very keen to stop.[2] Almost nine out of ten (88%) of smokers state that they want to quit because of a health concern. After health reasons, the next most common reason given for wanting to give up is a financial one.[2] The most important element of the cessation process is the smoker's decision to quit, with the aid or method of secondary importance. However, those who use aids such as nicotine replacement therapy double their chances of successfully quitting.[3] Smokers wishing to quit may find it helpful to telephone the national helpline on 0800 169 0169. Pregnant women seeking help in stopping smoking should call 0800 169 9169 where specialist counsellors are available from 1pm to 9pm, 7 days a week, to give advice. QUIT also operates specialist advice lines in the main Asian languages and in Turkish and Kurdish.

Beneficial health changes when you stop smoking

Stop smoking and the body will begin to repair the damage done almost immediately, kick-starting a series of beneficial health changes that continue for years.[4]

Time since quitting	Beneficial health changes that take place
20 minutes	Blood pressure and pulse rate return to normal.
8 hours	Nicotine and carbon monoxide levels in blood reduce by half, oxygen levels return to normal.
24 hours	Carbon monoxide will be eliminated from the body. Lungs start to clear out mucus and other smoking debris.
48 hours	There is no nicotine left in the body. Ability to taste and smell is greatly improved.
72 hours	Breathing becomes easier. Bronchial tubes begin to relax and energy levels increase.
2-12 weeks	Circulation improves.
3-9 months	Coughs, wheezing and breathing problems improve as lung function is increased by up to 10%.
1 year	Risk of heart attack falls to about half that of a smoker.
10 years	Risk of lung cancer falls to half of that of a smoker.
15 years	Risk of heart attack falls to the same as someone who has never smoked.

Practice Exam — Item B

Withdrawal symptoms

Withdrawal symptoms are the physical and mental changes that occur following interruption or termination of drug use. They are normally temporary and are a product of the physical or psychological adaptation to long-term drug use, requiring a period of re-adjustment when the drug is no longer ingested. In the case of smoking, some of these are:[5]

Withdrawal symptom	Duration	Proportion of those trying to quit who are affected
Irritability / aggression	Less than 4 weeks	50%
Depression	Less than 4 weeks	60%
Restlessness	Less than 4 weeks	60%
Poor concentration	Less than 2 weeks	60%
Increased appetite	Greater than 10 weeks	70%
Light-headedness	Less than 48 hours	10%
Night-time awakenings	Less than 1 week	25%
Craving	Greater than 2 weeks	70%

References

1. Nicotine Addiction in Britain. A report of the Royal College of Physicians, February 2000

2. Lader, D & Goddard, E. Smoking-related behaviour and attitudes, 2004. London, ONS, 2005

3. Smoking cessation guidelines and their cost effectiveness. Thorax 1998; vol 53: S5 (part 2) S11-S16

4. The Health Benefits of Smoking Cessation: A report of the Surgeon General. US DHHS, 1990.

5. West, R. Tobacco withdrawal symptoms. St. George's Hospital Medical School, 1996.

<u>*Acknowledgements*</u>

The Publisher would like to thank the following copyright holders for permission to reproduce texts and images:

<u>www.direct.gov.uk</u>
'Voluntary work abroad', www.direct.gov.uk © Crown Copyright

<u>Médecins Sans Frontières</u>
'Eyewitness' article © 2005 Médecins Sans Frontières

<u>Kadir van Lohuizen / Agence VU</u>
'Eyewitness' photograph © Kadir van Lohuizen / Agence VU

<u>NI Syndication</u>
'Cartoon duo play cat and mouse with PC police' © NI Syndication

<u>ASH (Action on Smoking and Health)</u>
Material reproduced with permission of ASH (Action on Smoking and Health)

Every effort has been made to locate copyright holders and obtain permission to reproduce texts and images. For those texts and images where it has been difficult to trace the originator of the work, we would be grateful for information. If any copyright holder would like us to make an amendment to the acknowledgements, please notify us and we will gladly update the book at the next reprint. Thank you.